Say 'Hello'
to Peter Ian Green
– 'PIG' for short.

There are six PIG books so far. It's best to read them in this order:

1. **Pig** and the **Talking Poo**
2. **Pig** and the **Fancy Pants**
3. **Pig** and the **Long Fart**
4. **Pig** plays **Cupid**
5. **Pig** gets the **Black Death** (nearly)
6. **Pig** Saves the **Day**

PIG and the Long Fart
by Barbara Catchpole
Illustrated by metaphrog

Published by Ransom Publishing Ltd.
Unit 7, Brocklands Farm, West Meon, Hampshire
GU32 1JN, UK
www.ransom.co.uk

ISBN   978 184167 524 4
First published in 2012
Reprinted 2013, 2015, 2016

PIG

and the
Long
Fart

Barbara Catchpole

Illustrated by metaphrog

Rans**m

4

Me

The most amazing, stupendous, epic stuff has been happening!

Peter Ian Green (Pig to you and, well, everyone else really) fell in love with a REAL girl. We were together for nearly a whole month.

Her name is Tiffany, she chews gum a lot and she's in the bottom Maths set.

She drew little pigs in hearts and 'TIFF + PIG 4EVA' in pink highlighter on her Maths book.

The teacher made her cover it with bits of wallpaper he had in his cupboard. (Teachers are quite sad aren't they? Like they have wallpaper left over from doing their hall and they bring it into school to cover books, instead of chucking it in the bin like normal not-sad people.)

6

Tiff and I sat together in the dining hall. We texted each other during 'Eastenders' and 'X Factor' – even when we watched them together on the settee round at Tiff's house.

Then last Thursday, after the Assembly to welcome the Mayor, she dumped me. She broke my heart and I will never love a girl again.

I think about her nearly every day.

I think she's going out with Dean Gosnall again
now. He's got really
big teeth and zits –
he looks like a spotty
Alvin the Chipmunk.
Oh, and he's captain
of the lower school
football team.

Dean Gosnall

My family

At the end of this story I'm going to tell you
what my family said about THE BREAK UP, so
that I have a proper ending and I don't have

to go dot dot dot.

Yes, thanks for asking, they're all fine. Gran's well over her flu, and on Monday we got the last bit of toffee out of the hamster's pouches with my sister Suki's eyebrow tweezers and a bit of toilet roll.

Mum's fingers have healed, too.

How are your lot?

My sister Suki has also had a bit of a romance. She got her earrings caught on this bloke's scarf on the bus and had to go all the way with him. That's all the way to the bus station with her head on his shoulder.

His name is Lee and he's got a job. He's a milkman. (Mum says she'll be OK for yoghurt!)

Lee's taking Suki to speedway on Friday, and he bought her a bracelet in Argos. She says he's alright in a poor light, she supposes.

Lee in a poor light.

I think it's a shame, because he's really keen on her and she never goes out with boys for very long. She says she doesn't see the point and they give her a headache.

Anyway, this story is about how Tiffany and I

got together, which is the happy bit. Then it is the story of how THE FART squeezed between us and drove us apart. Which is the sad bit and not at all funny like Raj thinks it is.

The poem

Raj and I were round his house and I was a bit down after the thing with the panties and the headteacher's toilet.

I had been put into the bottom Maths set. The headteacher taught divvy Maths and I'd been put in there because she

'wanted to keep an eye on you, young Peter'.

Anyway, the work was too easy for me. I was finished way before everyone else and had to do 'Extension Work' all the time, which means doing more of the same stuff.

My Mum was angry with me. She said:

'You're good at sums like your dad, wherever he is, the good-for-nothing loser,'

and

'He could settle a bet in his head while the bookie was still tapping away on his fancy computer,'

and

'Those teachers are holding you back,'

and

'I'm going up that school!'

She probably will. She's 'up that school' so often she might as well have her own space in the motorbike rack. They probably think she's one of the teachers.

The only good thing about the new class was Tiffany. Our eyes met across the plastic bricks and I fell in love.

She doesn't know her tables, but she knew the

way to my heart. She can't add up, but she multiplied the love I felt.

But how could I let her know I loved her? I couldn't just go

> 'Nine sevens are sixty three and I think I love you.'

or

> 'You've put the decimal place in the wrong place and I think you're hot!'

Raj said:

'You should write her a poem and put it in her locker, through the slots at the top. You stand a chance because she's just been dumped by Dean Gosnall.'

I took notice of what Raj said because he has seven sisters. If there is one thing Raj knows about, it's girls. He was the one that told me about thongs.

Mind you, having seven sisters has its downsides.
Raj has to wait so long to get into the bathroom
at home that sometimes he cleans his teeth
and does his morning loo stuff round our house
(in our bathroom of course, not in the kitchen).

Anyway, Raj said he was good at poems. I've
never seen any sign of this talent in English
lessons, but I let him have a go.

He thought a bit and wrote a poem for me:

FOR TIFFANY

Your eyes are like dark pools in the forest

Your lips are like strawberries in summer

I want to sit in front of Eastenders on

the settee in the lounge round your house

with you forever.

Now, I think we all know why Raj's poem is no good – there's no rhymes. Poems have to rhyme – or really what's the point? It was good and short though, and I do like that in a poem.

Raj got a bit moody when I pointed the rhyme thing out. He said I didn't know what I was

talking about. I thanked him nicely like Mum
says you should. But when I got home I wrote
my own poem:

FOR TIFF

Your eyes are nice

Your lips are yum

Your hair is cool

And I like your pencil case.

From Pig (new boy in Maths, told
you four eights last week).

I couldn't think of any rhymes. Well, I could
think of one, but that did seem a bit rude. And
anyway, she DID have a nice pencil case. But I

think the poem's a bit better than Raj's effort.

I tell Tiff I love her

I put the note in her locker. She loved it!

She said:

'This will show that Dean Gosnall.'

If this was a telly programme, it would go all wavy and fuzzy and then you would see all the things we did together while we were going out. You know, like CSI when they do all the boring bits in the lab before they discover the soil on the shoe can only come from one particular garden in the whole of New York. The garden just happens to belong to some creepy guy

whose picture they have on a computer.

It could have love music playing at the same

time - the pictures of Tiff and me, I mean,

not the computer pictures of the creep.

Tiff and I spent the whole time at school

holding hands. I only really let go of her when

she had to go to the toilet.

We even put our hands up in Maths, holding hands, when I knew an answer. She didn't ever know any answers, but I think she enjoyed the exercise.

My farting problem

I only had one problem. Well, two really, but one was linked to the other one. So it might be one. Or two. Or one.

Anyway, you must promise not to tell anyone because it is a bit gross. When I get nervous, my tummy gets upset and I fart a bit.

Tiffany made me nervous. Being in love is hard work and whenever I got scared I would mess it up. I couldn't work out what to do a lot of the time, because girls don't tell you what they are thinking. You have to guess.

For example:

'Do you want to watch the football?'

means

'I don't want to watch the football. Ever.'

and

'Does this look OK on me?'

means

'Tell me I look good!'

It's very difficult to get it right all the time and I got stressy. So I kept doing these little farts (just FARTLETS really).

(We did brackets in English this week. I don't like them as much as the dots.)

Or I kept letting the gas build up and then running to the toilets to get rid of it all in one go.

I don't think Tiffany noticed, because if she said anything like

'What's that smell?'

I would say something clever (and true) like

'Someone must have farted.'

Someone is always farting in that Maths set,

because it is mostly boys.

I don't suppose you've noticed, but girls don't

fart much. I don't know why girls wear smelly

stuff because they smell nice anyway. It's the boys who should wear smellies.

If a boy gets bored in lessons, he does a silent fart. It's just something to do. Not even the headteacher can prove it's you. Even if it makes a bit of a squeaky noise, as long as you don't look up, you're OK.

The second part of the problem was that Tiffany was chosen to do The Welcome Speech in assembly for the Mayor. She was always chosen for everything because she's pretty and because her mum is a Governor of the school (whatever that is).

When I told Mum she said

'That figures. Life is like that.'

Tiffany had to choose a partner to say some of the speech – and she chose me!

The headteacher was, like:

'Are you sure, Tiffany? PIG? Quite sure?'

and Tiffany goes:

'I only want to do it if Pig can do it, Miss.'

and Miss goes:

'Oh alright, Tiffany!'

and then she did that thing with her eyes that grown-ups do when they are not getting their own way.

Now, I get terrified doing an assembly. I feel sick just thinking about it. I said to Tiff:

'I can't do it, Tiff. I get nervous.'

She said:

'Then I'll have to find someone else!'

Her eyes were cold and her shiny (lip-glossed) mouth was in a straight line. She wasn't just talking about the assembly, I could tell.

I did a big fart and had to pretend I had coughed. I moved about a lot to get rid of the smell.

Beans for breakfast is not a good idea

I practised my line over and over:

'I am proud to take part in this assembly.'

'I am proud to take part in this assembly.'

'I am proud to take part in this assembly.'

My whole family was coming to watch, except Harry the Hamster – and my dad, of course.

We didn't know where Dad was – and we like to be quite sure where Harry is at all times.

Mum did us all a huge breakfast: sausages, eggs, fried bread and baked beans.

Then they all got 'tarted up' and we walked to school together – Mum, Gran, Suki and me. Of course it took ages because Gran only goes 'a mile a fortnight' and Suki wears five-inch heels.

My mum said it was

'like the slug Olympics'.

It was a really nice sunny morning and I wished I could stay out in it with my family for the whole day. We could go to the seaside.

When I thought
about the assembly,
it was like my
tummy turned over
(like when I went
down the helter

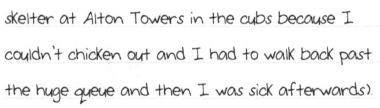

skelter at Alton Towers in the cubs because I couldn't chicken out and I had to walk back past the huge queue and then I was sick afterwards).

When we got to school, I had no time to go to the toilet and I really needed to go.

The assembly

By the time I was up on the stage for assembly, I will tell you a secret – I was terrified. We were using mikes because the hall is huge and nobody can hear you if you just shout.

If you just shout, then people get bored and they start to play around with the climbing ropes. They click at the top and are very noisy.

My family and Tiff's were in the front row and the headteacher and the Mayor and the top teachers were on the stage to one side.

I looked out at all the faces. This was my world – all in front of me. Nearly everyone I knew, all looking at me in silence.

I felt my tummy start to make gas. I could feel it bubbling its way down. Tiffany and I stood up. I had to squeeze my bottom together to hold it all in. I really, really needed to fart. I was concentrating REALLY hard.

I was thinking about my tummy so much that, when I stood up, I said loudly right into the mike:

'I am proud to take fart in this assembly ...'

Then I was so shocked by what I had said, I DID fart. A real, live, actual fart.

The mike picked it up and the noise filled the hall over the PA system. It was loud and you could really tell what it was. It seemed to go on and on and on forever. You know the kind I mean.

I just couldn't stop. It was like I exploded. It

was a bit of a smelly one too, and the people on the stage started fanning their faces with their hands and putting their hankies up to their noses. The headteacher sneezed.

Because I am ginger, I go really red quite easily, and that was what happened. I couldn't look. It's another secret, but I even felt like crying. I put my hands over my face and the Mayor got up quickly and walked across the stage.

He put his hand on my shoulder and said

'Better out than in, eh, lad?'

and went straight into his speech. Tiff never got to say her bit in assembly.

But she said plenty in the playground afterwards.

My family says

1.Mum

The first thing my mum did was go to reception and say she didn't want me punished as it wasn't my fault – I was nervous.

Usually the teachers don't take any notice of that, but the Mayor was there too and he agreed. He said he used to get gas when he was scared and his wife didn't talk to him for a week after their wedding.

I guess the headteacher thought it was best to let it go. I'm not allowed to do another assembly (boo hoo hoo) and I'm not allowed beans at school dinners any more (I bet they'll forget).

Oh, and they moved me back up into my old Maths set because the headteacher said I was 'A Bad Influence on Tiffany'.

I think her family asked for me to be moved. My heart is breaking and nobody cares.

I told Mum how badly I had upset Tiffany and she said:

'Our hamster has got more brains than that girl.'

and:

'It was her own fault because she tried to change you!'

and:

'The only time a woman can change a man is her son when he's still in nappies.'

and:

'You have to love them just as they are.'

Then she went very quiet.

2. Harry (the hamster — in case you forgot)

I asked him what he thought. He was asleep. I woke him up and he bit me.

3. Gran

Gran said it was the best school 'do' she'd ever been to. She said she hadn't laughed so much for ages. She told me some rhymes:

Beans, beans, the musical fruit:

The more you eat, the more you toot!

The more you toot, the better you feel,

So let's have beans for every meal!

and

Wherever you are or whoever you may be

Let your wind blow free!

She knows some cool poetry. Some of it is a bit

rude, though. But it made me feel a lot better.

And you will notice that both of these poems rhyme. In your face, Raj!

4. Suki

Suki gave me a big hug and said I could go to speedway with her and Lee on Friday.

I said:

'Won't he mind?'

and she said:

'He won't if he knows what's good for him'.

I said I thought it was all over with Tiff. Suki
said she wasn't surprised.

She said:

'Love may be
blind, but it's still
got a sense of
smell'.

5. Me (again)

I don't think I'll ever get married – for three reasons:

Reason One

It's hard work talking to girls, because they are not interested in any cool stuff like football.

Reason Two

If you get divorced, you have to give her half your stuff and I'm not sawing the Talking Poo in half.

Reason Three

Girls make me fart.

Perhaps we'll just buy a dog and I'll blame it on him, because dogs are farty.

Perhaps I'll just buy a dog and not bother with a girl. Then we can sit and watch telly and fart together.

Beans make me fart too.

But I'm definitely not planning on marrying a bean.

The next **PIG** book is

PIG
plays
Cupid

About the author

Barbara Catchpole was a teacher for thirty years and enjoyed every minute. She has three sons of her own who were always perfectly behaved and never gave her a second of worry.

Barbara also tells lies.

How many have you read?

and the
Talking Poo

Barbara Catchpole

and the
Fancy Pants

Barbara Catchpole

and the
Long Fart

plays
Cupid

Barbara Catchpole

gets the
Black Death
(nearly)

Barbara Catchpole

Saves
the Day

Barbara Catchpole

and the
Ice-cream
Cake

Barbara Catchpole

Skives
off School

is a
Blue Baboon's
Bottom

Barbara Catchpole

SuperPig!

Barbara Catchpole

and the Baldy Cat

Barbara Catchpole

Leaves Home (for a bit)

Barbara Catchpole

Whopping Great Fib

Barbara Catchpole

is Hairy Snotter

Barbara Catchpole

and the Rainbow Hair

Barbara Catchpole

and the Big Quiz

Barbara Catchpole

Gets Angry

Barbara Catchpole

Season's Finale

Barbara Catchpole

Say 'hello' to

Feely

Feely's Magic Diary
Barbara Catchpole

Feely for Prime Minister
Barbara Catchpole

Feely and her Well-Mad Parents
Barbara Catchpole

How many have you read?